LUDWIG VAN BEETHOVEN

QUARTET

for 2 Violins, Viola and Violoncello
C♯ minor/cis-Moll/Ut♯ mineur
Op. 131

Edited by/Herausgegeben von
Wilhelm Altmann

T0081295

Ernst Eulenburg Ltd

London · Mainz · Madrid · New York · Paris · Prague · Tokyo · Toronto · Zürich

L. van BEETHOVEN
String Quartet in C sharp minor, Op. 131

Immediately after Beethoven had finished the last of the three quartets dedicated to Prince Galitzin (No. 1, op. 127, No. 2, op. 132, No. 3, op. 130) including the great fugue (op. 135) as a finale, he devoted himself–at the latest in March 1826–to the composition of the C sharp minor quartet, a work, to outward appearances, of a totally different character. Although, from its form, this work bears the semblance of improvisation, Beethoven worked hard at it, and took special pains with the variation movement, as may be gathered by the sketches in Nottebohm's "Beethoviana" page 54.

On May 20th 1826 the quartet was offered to Schott, the publisher in Mainz, for the price of 80 ducats; this sum was paid to the composer, arrangements being completed by July 16th 1826.

In the "Intelligenzblatt der Caecilia" (Annual Series VII, No. 25), the following announcement, on pages 31/32, from the publishers B. Schott's Söhne may be found:

"Missa solemnis in D major by Ludwig van Beethoven op. 123 and his last Quartet for 2 Violins, Viola and Violoncello in C sharp minor op. 129.–With pride we can inform the public that Beethoven's last Quartet (in C sharp minor op. 129, for 2 Violins, Viola and Violoncello) has been published by us and forwarded to all music warehouses of note, as well as the score of this masterpiece. Mainz, April 1827."

The error in the opus number (129 instead of 131) was later rectified.

The title of the work (first edition of the parts) runs as follows:

Grand Quatuor En Ut dièce mineur pour deux Violons Alto et Violoncelle composé et dédié à Son Excellence Monsieur Le Baron de Stutterheim, Lieutenant-Maréchal de Camp Impérial et Royal d'Autriche. Conseiller aulique actuel de Guerre, Commandeur de l'ordre

Gleich nachdem Beethoven das letzte der drei für den Fürsten Galitzin bestimmten Quartette (Nr. 1 = op. 127, Nr. 2 = op. 132. Nr. 3 = op. 130) beendet hatte, und zwar mit der großen Fuge (op. 135) als Finale, spätestens im März 1826, ging er an die Komposition des in der äußeren Form ganz abweichenden Cis-moll-Quartetts. Obwohl dieses seiner Gestaltung nach den Eindruck einer Improvisation macht, hat er doch ungemein viel daran gearbeitet, besonders an dem Variationensatz, wie man sich aus den bei Nottebohm, Beethoviana S. 54 ff. überzeugen kann.

Angeboten hat er es am 20. Mai 1826 dem Verlag Schott in Mainz für 80 Dukaten, die ihm auch gezahlt wurden; am 16. Juli 1826 meldet er die Fertigstellung.

Im „Intelligenzblatt der Caecilia" Jahrgang VII, No. 25, findet sich auf Seite 31/32 folgende Anzeige der Verlagsfirma B. Schott's Söhne:

„Missa solemnis in D-dur von Ludwig van Beethoven op. 123 und dessen letztes Quartett für 2 Violinen, Viola und Violoncell aus cis-moll op. 129. – Wir sind stolz darauf, zugleich anzeigen zu können, daß auch Beethovens letztes Quartett (aus cis - moll, op. 129, für 2 Violinen, Viola und Vcell.) ebenfalls bei uns erschienen und, an alle soliden Musikhandlungen bereits versendet ist und auch die Partitur dieses letzten Meisterwerkes. Mainz, im April 1827."

Dieser Irrtum in der Opuszahl (129 statt 131) wurde später korrigiert.

Der Titel der Erst-Ausgabe (in Stimmen) lautet:

Grand Quatuor En Ut dièce mineur pour deux Violons Alto et Violoncelle composé et dédié à Son Excellence Monsieur Le Baron de Stutterheim, Lieutenant-Maréchal de Camp Impérial et Royal d'Autriche. Conseiller aulique actuel de Guerre, Commandeur de l'ordre de Leopold d'Autriche, Chevalier de de Leopold d'Autriche. Chevalier de l'ordre militaire de Marie Thérèse et de l'ordre Impériale de Wladimir de Russie de la 3me Classe. Grand-Croix de l'ordre Royal de Sardaigne de Maurice et Lazare, et de l'ordre Royal militaire de St. George de la Réunion de Sicile, deuxième propriétaire de 8me Regiment d'Infanterie de ligne Impérial et Royal par Louis van Beethoven Oeuvre 131. Propriété des Editeurs. Mayence chez les fils de B. Schott à Paris, rue de Bourbon No. 17, à Anvers, chez A. Schott. (Parts No. 2628, Score No. 2692)

This quartet was intended originally to be dedicated to Joh. Wolfmeier, to whom, however op. 135 was finally inscribed.

l'ordre militaire de Marie Thérèse et de l'ordre Impériale de Wladimir de Russie de la 3me Classe. Grand-Croix de l'ordre Royal de Sardaigne de Maurice et Lazare, et de l'ordre Royal militaire de St. George de la Réunion de Sicile, deuxième propriétaire de 8me Regiment d'Infanterie de ligne Impérial et Royal par Louis van Beethoven Oeuvre 131. Propriété des Editeurs. Mayence chez les fils de B. Schott à Paris rue de Bourbon No. 17, à Anvers, chez A. Schott. (Verlags-No. der Stimmen: 2628, der Partitur 2692.)

Ursprünglich sollte dieses Quartett Joh. Wolfmeier gewidmet werden, der dann durch die Dedikation von op. 135 entschädigt wurde.

Quartet

L. van Beethoven, Op. 131.
1770-1827.

Nº 1. Adagio, ma non troppo e molto espressivo.

E. E. 1102

2

No 2. Allegro molto vivace.

un poco rit.

in tempo

poco rit. in tempo

E.E.1102

Nº 4. Andante, ma non troppo e molto cantabile.

Adagio.

Allegretto.

Adagio, ma non troppo e semplice.

22

2-3

Nº 5. Presto.

Ritmo di quattro battute.

34

Molto poco adagio.

E. E. 1102

36

E.E.1102

N⁰ 6. Adagio quasi un poco andante.

Nº 7. Allegro.

40

E.E. 1102

42

F.E.1102

non ligato

E.E. 1102

48